Contents

Minutes in an hour

The marks around the edge of a clock face show the **minutes**.

The big hand moves **clockwise** and counts the minutes.

There are **60** minutes in an **hour**.

The small hand moves clockwise very slowly and counts the hours.

(1) Count in 5s around the clock face and write the missing minutes. Make sure you count clockwise.

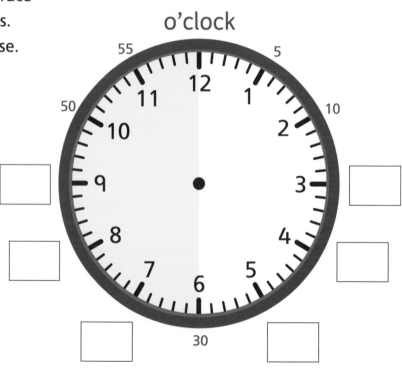

Did you know?

The word 'minute' comes from the Latin word 'minutus', which means 'small'.

Schofield&Sims

Telling the Time 2

Name _____

Note for teachers and parents

Learning to tell the time is a complex process that many children need help to grasp. This series breaks down telling the time into very small steps that every child can understand. Featuring clear step-by-step learning, varied practice activities and fun time facts, these workbooks provide everything children need to master this essential life skill.

Telling the Time 2 introduces children to counting in 5s around the clock and the related minutes-past and minutes-to times. Digital time is introduced and the children start to make comparisons between analogue and digital clocks. There are also problem-solving challenges with questions that ask how much time has passed between two given times. This book supports the National Curriculum for Mathematics at Key Stage 1, but it can also be used with older children who require additional support.

Try to discuss time as often as you can with the child and draw attention to different means of time-telling such as a clock on the wall, a wristwatch, or time displays on phones and computers. Questions such as "What time is bedtime?" and "How long does it take to get to school?" will help the child to think about the importance of time measurement and to become familiar with vocabulary that relates to time.

Each book features large clock faces that little fingers can easily count on. When introducing each new time, encourage the child to count aloud and point to the numbers around the edge of the clock. This will help to secure the idea that the hands of the clock are constantly moving around the circle of the clock face. The hands of the clock are colour-coded throughout the series – blue for the minute hand and red for the hour hand – to help the child to identify them quickly.

Children are given frequent opportunities to practise their learning through a variety of activities, such as drawing the hands on the clock, matching activities, mazes, and word and number problems. You will find answers to all the activities at the back of the book.

Published by **Schofield & Sims Ltd**, Dogley Mill, Fenay Bridge, Huddersfield HD8 0NQ, UK
Telephone 01484 607080
www.schofieldandsims.co.uk

This edition copyright © Schofield & Sims Ltd, 2017
First published in 2017

Author: **Christine Shaw**
Christine Shaw has asserted her moral rights under the Copyright, Designs and Patents Act, 1988, to be identified as the author of this work.

British Library Cataloguing in Publication Data
A catalogue record for this book is available from the British Library.

Design by **Oxford Designers & Illustrators Ltd**

Printed in the UK by **Page Bros (Norwich) Ltd**

ISBN 978 07217 1419 6

Counting in 5s

Learn

To tell the time you need to be able to count in 5s.

5, 10, 15, 20, 25, 30, 35, 40, 45, 50, 55, 60

1 Count in 5s. Write the missing numbers in each sequence.

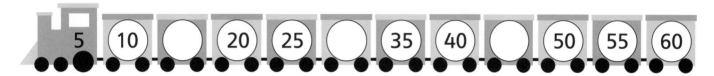

5, 10, ◯, 20, 25, ◯, 35, 40, ◯, 50, 55, 60

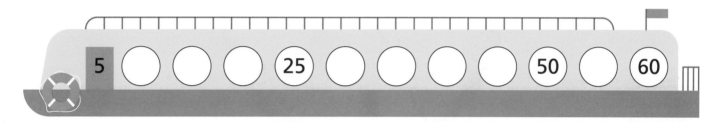

5, ◯, ◯, ◯, 25, ◯, ◯, ◯, ◯, 50, ◯, 60

2 Count in 5s to help the bee reach the beehive. Draw a line to show the way.

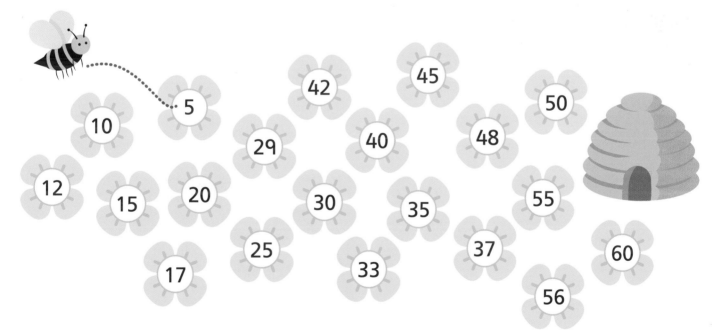

3 Count on in 5s. Write the missing numbers.

5 → ☐   20 → ☐   10 → ☐

35 → ☐   50 → ☐   15 → ☐

5 minutes past

Count in 5s the minutes from o'clock to the big hand. Make sure you count clockwise.

o'clock

The big hand has moved 5 minutes on from o'clock. When the big hand is here, it shows 5 minutes past.

The small hand counts the hours. It has only just left 7. It is 5 minutes past 7.

(1) Draw the hands on the clock to show 5 minutes past 2.
Can you see where to put the small hand?

5 minutes past

(2) What time is it?

It is 5 minutes past _____ .

It is _____ minutes past _____ .

It is _____ .

It is _____ .

(3) Draw lines to match each clock to the correct time.

It is 5 minutes past 8.

It is 5 minutes past 11.

It is 5 minutes past 2.

Did you know?

People who live near the sea can often tell the time by watching the tide come in and go out.

10 minutes past

Count in 5s the minutes from o'clock to the big hand.

o'clock

The big hand has moved 10 minutes on from o'clock. When the big hand is here, it shows 10 minutes past.

The small hand has moved to just after 7. It is 10 minutes past 7.

(1) Draw the hands on the clock to show 10 minutes past 5.
Can you see where to put the small hand?

10 minutes past

(2) What time is it?

It is 10 minutes past _____ .

It is _____ minutes past _____ .

It is _____ .

It is _____ .

(3) Draw a line to match the picture to the correct clock.

15 minutes past

Learn

Count in 5s the minutes from o'clock to the big hand.

o'clock

The big hand has moved 15 minutes on from o'clock. It has gone a quarter of the way around the clock. When the big hand is here, it shows 15 minutes past.

Look where the small hand is. It has moved further away from 7.

It is 15 minutes past 7. People usually call this time quarter past 7.

(1) Draw the hands on the clock to show 15 minutes past 9.
Can you see where to put the small hand?

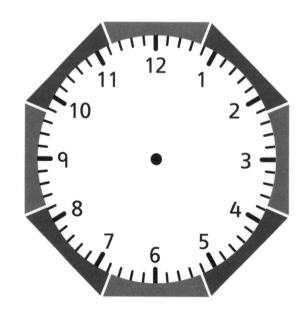

15 minutes past

(2) What time is it?

It is quarter past _____ .

It is _____ minutes past _____ .

It is _____ .

It is _____ .

(3) Draw lines to match each clock to the correct time.

| It is quarter past 12. | It is quarter past 10. | It is quarter past 5. |

20 minutes past

Count in 5s the minutes from o'clock to the big hand.

o'clock

The big hand has moved 20 minutes on from o'clock. When the big hand is here, it shows 20 minutes past.

The small hand has moved even further away from 7. It is 20 minutes past 7.

(1) Draw the hands on the clock to show 20 minutes past 1.
Can you see where to put the small hand?

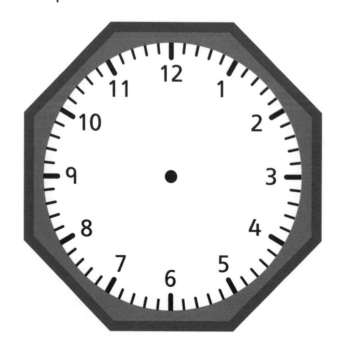

20 minutes past

(2) What time is it?

It is 20 minutes past _____ .

It is _____ minutes past _____ .

It is _____ .

It is _____ .

(3) Complete the maze to find out what time the alarm clock will ring.
Then draw the hands on the clock to show this time.

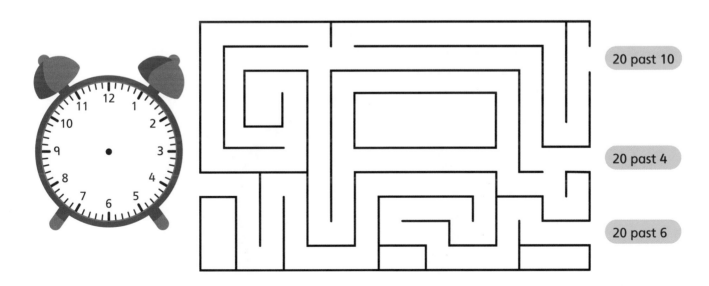

20 past 10

20 past 4

20 past 6

25 minutes past

Count in 5s the minutes from o'clock to the big hand.

o'clock

The big hand has moved 25 minutes on from o'clock. When the big hand is here, it shows 25 minutes past.

The small hand is nearly halfway between 7 and 8. It is 25 minutes past 7.

① Draw the hands on the clock to show 25 minutes past 4.
Can you see where to put the small hand?

14   Schofield & Sims Telling the Time 2

25 minutes past

2 What time is it?

It is 25 minutes past _____ .

It is _____ minutes past _____ .

It is _____ .

It is _____ .

3 Tick the clocks that show 25 minutes past.

☐

☐

☐

30 minutes past

Count in 5s the minutes from o'clock to the big hand.

o'clock

The big hand has moved 30 minutes on from o'clock. It has gone halfway around the clock face. When the big hand is here, it shows 30 minutes past.

The small hand is halfway between 7 and 8.

It is 30 minutes past 7. People usually call this time half past 7.

1 Draw the hands on the clock to show 30 minutes past 8.
Can you see where to put the small hand?

30 minutes past

2 What time is it?

It is half past _____ .

It is _____ minutes past _____ .

It is _____ .

It is _____ .

3 Draw a line to match the picture to the correct clock.

Mixed practice: tell the time 1

1 What time is it?

It is _____ minutes past _____ .

It is _____ .

It is _____ .

It is _____ .

2 Draw lines to match each clock to the correct time.

It is quarter past 7.

It is half past 8.

It is 25 minutes past 4.

Time sequences 1

(1) Add the missing times to each sequence.

6 o'clock, 5 minutes past 6, 10 minutes past 6, _____,

_____ , _____

10 minutes past 1, 15 minutes past 1, _____ ,

_____ , _____

5 minutes past 5, 10 minutes past 5, _____ ,

_____ , _____

(2) Put these clocks forward by 1 hour. Draw the hands on each clock below.

(3) **Earlier** or **later**? Write the correct word in each sentence.
All these times are in the morning.

9 o'clock is _____ than 5 minutes past 9.

5 minutes past 5 is _____ than 10 minutes past 5.

Half past 6 is _____ than 6 o'clock.

10 minutes past 7 is _____ than 20 minutes past 7.

Digital time

Learn

This is an **analogue** clock.
It has a big hand and a small hand.

This is a **digital** clock.
It has only numbers.

These clocks show the same time.

It is 4 o'clock. In digital time this is written as 4:00.

These clocks show the same time.

It is 5 minutes past 8. In digital time this is written as 8:05.

When you write digital time you write the hour first and then
the minutes past.

(1) Read each digital clock and write the time in digital time.

It is _____ : _____.   It is _____ : _____.   It is _____ : _____.

Digital time

2 Draw lines to match the clocks that show the same time.

3 What time is it?

It is _____ o'clock.

It is 2 : _____ .

It is _____ minutes past _____ .

It is _____ : _____ .

It is _____ minutes past _____ .

It is _____ : _____ .

It is _____ minutes past _____ .

It is _____ : _____ .

35 minutes past

Count in 5s the minutes from o'clock to the **big hand**. Make sure you count clockwise.

o'clock

The **big hand** has moved **35 minutes** on from o'clock. When the **big hand** is here, it shows **35 minutes past**.

The **small hand** is just over halfway between **4** and **5**.

It is **35 minutes past 4**.

In digital time this is **4:35**.

1 What time is it?

It is 35 minutes past _____.

It is 7 : _____.

It is _____ minutes past _____.

It is _____ : _____.

It is _____.

It is _____ : _____.

It is _____.

It is _____ : _____.

40 minutes past

Count in 5s the minutes from o'clock to the **big hand**.

o'clock

The **big hand** has moved **40 minutes** on from o'clock. When the **big hand** is here, it shows **40 minutes past**.

The **small hand** is getting closer to **5**.

It is **40 minutes past 4**.

In digital time this is **4:40**.

(1) Draw the hands on the clock to show 40 minutes past 4.
Write numbers on the digital clock to show the same time.

45 minutes past

Count in 5s the minutes from o'clock to the big hand.

o'clock

The big hand has moved 45 minutes on from o'clock. When the big hand is here, it shows 45 minutes past.

Look where the small hand is. It has moved even closer to 5.

It is 45 minutes past 4.

In digital time this is 4:45.

(1) Tick the clock that does <u>not</u> show 45 minutes past.

Shadows change in length and position throughout the day. The ancient Egyptians used this fact to make the first sundials.

50 minutes past

Count in 5s the minutes from o'clock
to the big hand.

o'clock

The big hand has moved 50 minutes on from o'clock. When the big hand is
here, it shows 50 minutes past.

The small hand is very nearly at 5.

It is 50 minutes past 4.

In digital time this is 4:50.

---

(1) Draw lines to match the clocks that show the same time.

55 minutes past

Count in 5s the minutes from o'clock to the big hand.

o'clock

The big hand has moved 55 minutes on from o'clock. When the big hand is here, it shows 55 minutes past.

The small hand is just before 5.

It is 55 minutes past 4.

In digital time this is 4:55.

---

(1) Tick the clocks that show 55 minutes past 9.

 ☐

 ☐

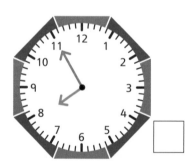 ☐

Did you know?

Sand timers were an early type of clock called 'hourglasses'. When all the sand ran from the top part into the bottom, an hour had passed.

Mixed practice: tell the time 2

1 What time is it? Write the time in digital time.

It is _____ : _____.

It is _____ : _____.

It is _____ : _____.

It is _____ : _____.

It is _____ : _____.

It is _____ : _____.

Time sequences 2

(1) Add the missing times to each sequence.

7 o'clock, 5 minutes past 7, 10 minutes past 7, _____,

_____, _____

25 minutes past 3, 30 minutes past 3, _____,

_____, _____

6:05, 6:10, 6:15, 6:20, _____, _____, _____

11:35, 11:40, 11:45, 11:50, _____, _____, _____

(2) Put these clocks back by 1 hour. Draw the hands or write the numbers on each clock below.

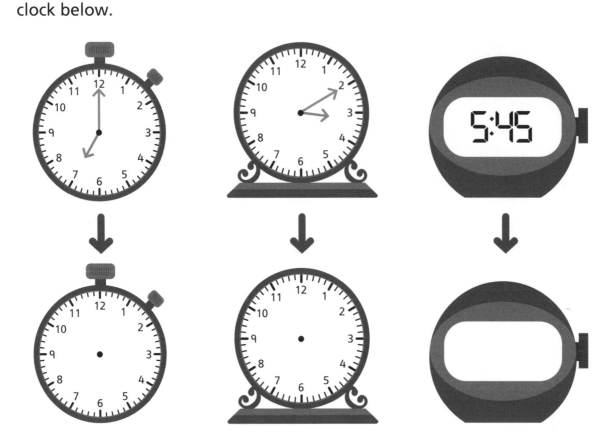

(3) **Earlier** or **later**? Write the correct word in each sentence. All these times are at night.

50 minutes past 1 is _____ than 55 minutes past 1.

Quarter past 8 is _____ than 10 minutes past 8.

11:40 is _____ than 11:45.

8:30 is _____ than 7:30.

Schofield & Sims Telling the Time 2

Minutes to

Learn

This clock shows **35 minutes past 12.**

This time also has another name:
25 minutes to 1.

When the **big hand** is in the shaded half of the clock, you can count in 5s <u>back</u> from o'clock to find the number of **minutes to** the next o'clock. This direction is called **anticlockwise**.

(1) Count in 5s back from o'clock to half past and write the missing minutes. Make sure you count anticlockwise.

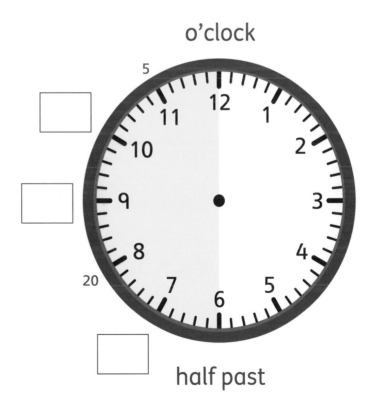

25 minutes to

Count in 5s the minutes from o'clock to the big hand.

The big hand has 25 minutes to go until the next o'clock. When the big hand is here, it is 25 minutes to.

Look at the small hand. It is just over halfway between 1 and 2.

It is 25 minutes to 2.

Remember, this is 1:35 in digital time.

(1) Draw the hands on the clock to show 25 minutes to 7.
Can you see where to put the small hand?

25 minutes to

(2) What time is it?

It is 25 minutes to _____ .

It is _____ minutes to _____ .

It is _____ .

It is _____ .

(3) Draw lines to match the clocks that show the same time.

20 minutes to

Learn

Count in 5s the minutes from o'clock to the big hand.

The big hand has 20 minutes to go until the next o'clock. When the big hand is here, it is 20 minutes to.

Look at the small hand. It is getting closer to 2.

It is 20 minutes to 2.

Remember, this is 1:40 in digital time.

1 Draw the hands on the clock to show 20 minutes to 10. Can you see where to put the small hand?

20 minutes to

(2) What time is it?

It is 20 minutes to _____ .

It is _____ minutes to _____ .

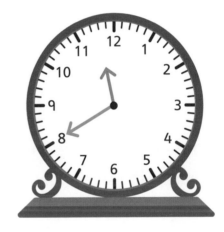

It is _____ .

It is _____ .

(3) Tick the clock that does <u>not</u> show 20 minutes to.

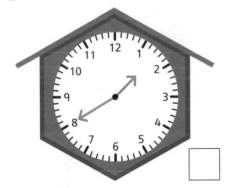

Did you know?

Grandfather clocks are tall clocks with a swinging pendulum. Each swing counts 1 second. The sound of the pendulum gives us the words 'tick tock'.

15 minutes to

Count in 5s the minutes from o'clock to the big hand.

The big hand has 15 minutes to go until the next o'clock. It has a quarter of the way around the clock still to go. When the big hand is here, it is 15 minutes to.

Look where the small hand is. It has moved even closer to 2.

It is 15 minutes to 2. People usually call this time quarter to 2.

Remember, this is 1:45 in digital time.

(1) Draw the hands on the clock to show 15 minutes to 6.
Can you see where to put the small hand?

Schofield & Sims Telling the Time 2

15 minutes to

(2) What time is it?

It is quarter to _____ .

It is 15 minutes to _____ .

It is _____ .

It is _____ .

(3) Draw lines to match each clock to the correct time.

| It is quarter to 1. | It is quarter to 6. | It is quarter to 11. |

10 minutes to

Count in 5s the minutes from o'clock to the big hand.

o'clock

The big hand has 10 minutes to go until the next o'clock. When the big hand is here, it is 10 minutes to.

Look at the small hand. It is very nearly at 2.

It is 10 minutes to 2.

Remember, this is 1:50 in digital time.

(1) Draw the hands on the clock to show 10 minutes to 3.
Can you see where to put the small hand?

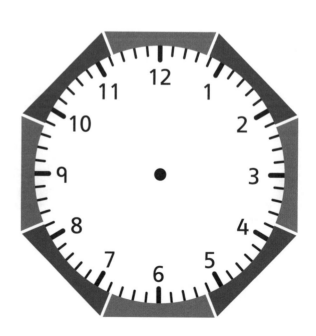

10 minutes to

(2) What time is it?

It is 10 minutes to _____ .

It is _____ minutes to _____ .

It is _____ .

It is _____ .

(3) Tick the clocks that show 10 minutes to 12.

 ☐

 ☐

 ☐

5 minutes to

Count in 5s the minutes from o'clock to the big hand.

o'clock

The big hand has 5 minutes to go until the next o'clock. When the big hand is here, it is 5 minutes to.

Look at the small hand. It is just before 2.

It is 5 minutes to 2.

Remember, this is 1:55 in digital time.

(1) Draw the hands on the clock to show 5 minutes to 5.
Can you see where to put the small hand?

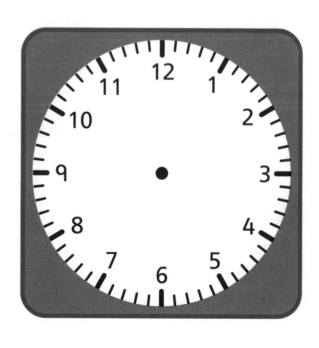

5 minutes to

(2) What time is it?

It is 5 minutes to _____.

It is _____ minutes to _____.

It is _____.

It is _____.

(3) **True** or **false**? Tick the correct answer.

It is 5 minutes to 9.

True ☐ False ☐

It is 5 minutes to 12.

True ☐ False ☐

Did you know?

The oldest working clock in the world stands in Salisbury Cathedral in England.

Mixed practice: tell the time 3

1 What time is it?

It is _____ .

It is _____ .

8:55

5:05

It is _____ .

It is _____ .

7:50

It is _____ .

It is _____ .

Mixed practice: tell the time 3

(2) Draw the hands on each clock to show the correct time.

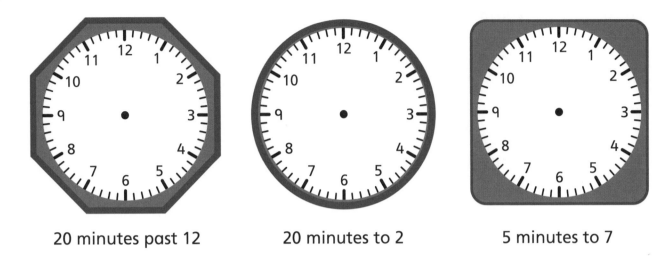

20 minutes past 12   20 minutes to 2   5 minutes to 7

(3) Write the numbers on each digital clock to show the correct time.

quarter past 8   25 minutes to 11   10 minutes to 1

(4) Complete the maze to find out what time the plane will leave. Then write the numbers on the clock to show this time.

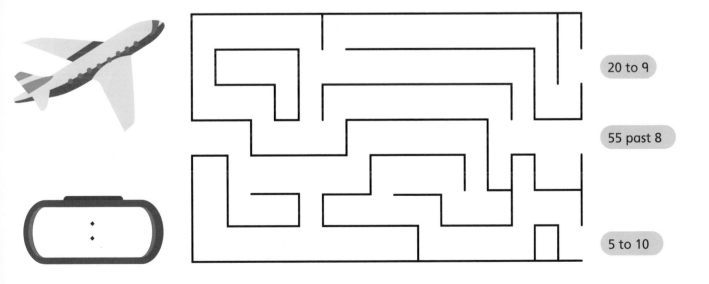

20 to 9

55 past 8

5 to 10

Time sequences 3

(1) Add the missing times to each sequence.

9:10, 9:15, 9:20, 9:25, _____, _____, _____

half past 12, 25 minutes to 1, _____,

_____, _____

3:40, 3:45, 3:50, 3:55, _____, _____, _____

quarter to 7, 10 minutes to 7, 5 minutes to 7, _____,

_____, _____

(2) Add the missing time to each sequence. Draw the hands or write the numbers.

(3) Put these clocks back by 1 hour. Draw the hands or write the numbers on each clock below.

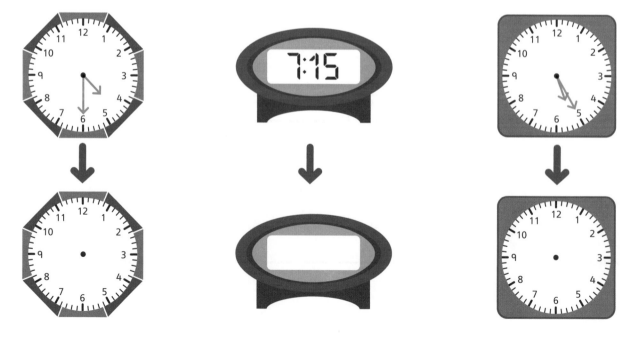

Lengths of time

1 How much time has passed between the first and second clocks?

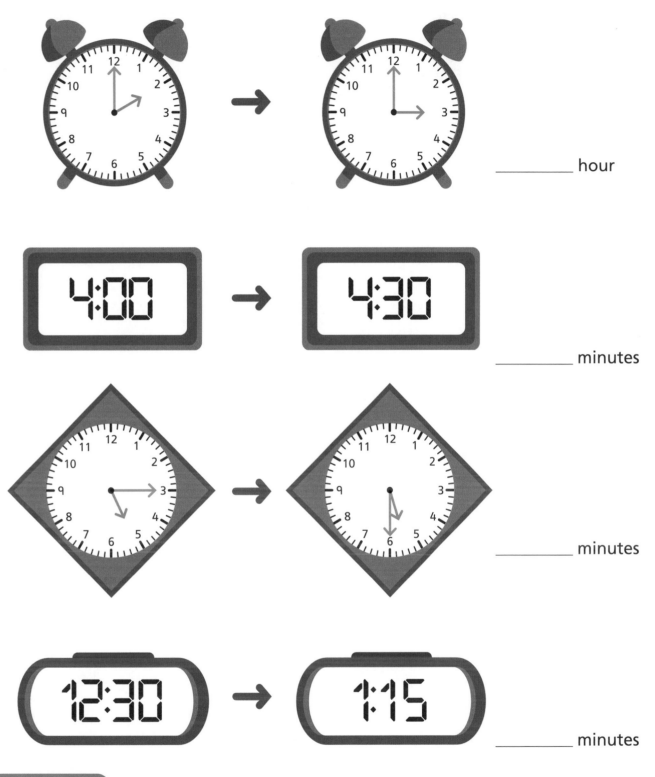

_____ hour

_____ minutes

_____ minutes

_____ minutes

Did you know?

Stopwatches show you how much time has passed. You start the stopwatch when an event begins and stop it at the end. Athletes use these to measure their speed.

Ordering and comparing time

Learn

There are **60 minutes** in an **hour.**
The big hand goes all the way around the clock <u>once</u> in an hour.

There are **24 hours** in a **day.**
The small hand goes all the way around the clock <u>twice</u> in a day.

(1) Draw a line to join these lengths of time in order from shortest to longest.

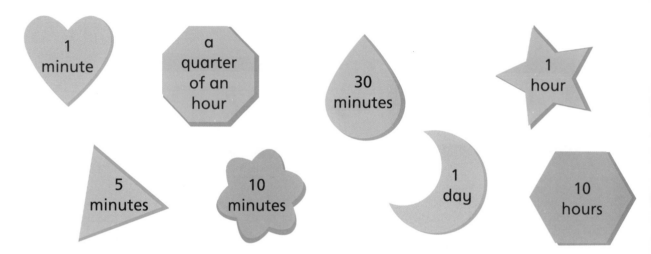

1 minute

a quarter of an hour

30 minutes

1 hour

5 minutes

10 minutes

1 day

10 hours

(2) Rosie and Viktor are doing homework.
Rosie takes 10 minutes to do her homework.
Viktor takes a quarter of an hour.

Who takes longer? _____

(3) Three runners ran in a race. Their times are below.

Alfie 40 minutes   Anya 35 minutes   Lexi 60 minutes

Who won the race? _____

Who came last in the race? _____

(4) Jordan and Maya are each baking a cake.
Jordan takes an hour and a half to finish his cake.
Maya takes an hour and 15 minutes.

Who takes longer? _____

Schofield & Sims Telling the Time 2

Answers

Page 4

1 The child counts the numbers around the clock in a clockwise direction.
15, 20, 25, 35, 40, 45

Page 5

1 15, 30, 45
10, 15, 20, 30, 35, 40, 45, 55

2 5, 10, 15, 20, 25, 30, 35, 40, 45, 50, 55, 60

3 10   25   15
40   55   20

Pages 6–7

1

2 5 minutes past 12, 5 minutes past 6, 5 minutes past 9, 5 minutes past 5

3
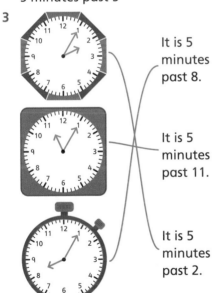

It is 5 minutes past 8.

It is 5 minutes past 11.

It is 5 minutes past 2.

Pages 8–9

1

2 10 minutes past 1, 10 minutes past 7, 10 minutes past 12, 10 minutes past 8

3

Pages 10–11

1
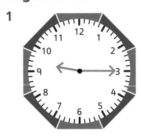

2 quarter past 6, 15 minutes past 1, quarter past 2/15 minutes past 2, quarter past 9/15 minutes past 9

3
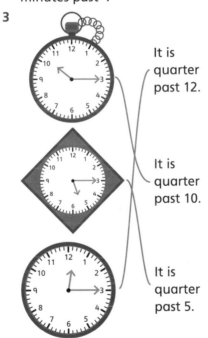

It is quarter past 12.

It is quarter past 10.

It is quarter past 5.

Pages 12–13

1

2 20 minutes past 9, 20 minutes past 12, 20 minutes past 7, 20 minutes past 11

3 route correctly drawn through maze to lead to 20 past 6

Pages 14–15

1

2 25 minutes past 1, 25 minutes past 6, 25 minutes past 8, 25 minutes past 12

3

☑   ☑

Pages 16–17

1

2 half past 4, 30 minutes past 10, half past 1/30 minutes past 1, half past 8/30 minutes past 8

Answers

3

Page 18

1 5 minutes past 6, quarter past 10/15 minutes past 10, 25 minutes past 2, 10 minutes past 5

2

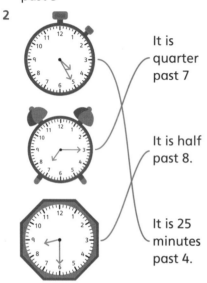

It is quarter past 7

It is half past 8.

It is 25 minutes past 4.

Page 19

1 quarter past 6/15 minutes past 6, 20 minutes past 6, 25 minutes past 6
20 minutes past 1, 25 minutes past 1, half past 1/30 minutes past 1
quarter past 5/15 minutes past 5, 20 minutes past 5, 25 minutes past 5

2

3 earlier, earlier, later, earlier,

Pages 20–21

1 1:00, 5:05, 3:30

2

3 2 o'clock, 2:00; 10 minutes past 11, 11:10; 20 minutes past 7, 7:20; 25 minutes past 5, 5:25

Page 22

1 35 minutes past 7, 7:35;
35 minutes past 10, 10:35;
35 minutes past 12, 12:35;
35 minutes past 2, 2:35

Page 23

1

Page 24

1

Page 25

1

Page 26

1

Page 27

1 2:40, 6:25, 11:35, 8:50, 1:10, 3:20

Page 28

1 quarter past 7/15 minutes past 7, 20 minutes past 7, 25 minutes past 7
35 minutes past 3, 40 minutes past 3, 45 minutes past 3
6:25, 6:30, 6:35
11:55, 12:00, 12:05

2

3 earlier, later, earlier, later

Page 29

1 The child counts anticlockwise from 12 to 6 on the clock.
10, 15, 25

Pages 30–31

1

2 25 minutes to 2, 25 minutes to 10, 25 minutes to 8/7:35, 25 minutes to 11/10:35

3

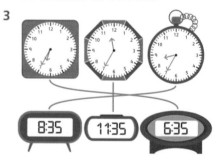

Pages 32–33

1

Answers

2 20 minutes to 5, 20 minutes to 9, 20 minutes to 1/12:40, 20 minutes to 12/11:40

3

Pages 34–35

1

2 quarter to 2, 15 minutes to 8, quarter to 1/15 minutes to 1/12:45, quarter to 7/15 minutes to 7/6:45

3

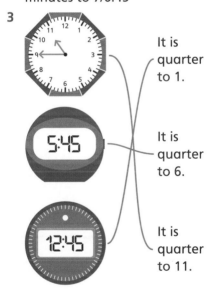

It is quarter to 1.

It is quarter to 6.

It is quarter to 11.

Pages 36–37

1

2 10 minutes to 11, 10 minutes to 6, 10 minutes to 1/12:50, 10 minutes to 9/8:50

3

Pages 38–39

1

2 5 minutes to 7, 5 minutes to 1, 5 minutes to 3/2:55, 5 minutes to 12/11:55

3 True, False

Pages 40–41

1 25 minutes past 6/6:25, 20 minutes to 3/40 minutes past 2/2:40, 5 minutes to 9/55 minutes past 8/8:55, 5 minutes past 5/5:05, 25 minutes to 4/35 minutes past 3/3:35, 10 minutes to 8/50 minutes past 7/7:50

2

3

4 route correctly drawn through maze to lead to 5 to 10

Page 42

1 9:30, 9:35, 9:40
20 minutes to 1, quarter to 1/15 minutes to 1, 10 minutes to 1
4:00, 4:05, 4:10
7 o'clock, 5 minutes past 7, 10 minutes past 7

2

3

Page 43

1 1 hour, 30 minutes, 15 minutes, 45 minutes

Page 44

1 1 minute, 5 minutes, 10 minutes, a quarter of an hour, 30 minutes, 1 hour, 10 hours, 1 day

2 Viktor

3 Anya, Lexi

4 Jordan

Schofield&Sims

the long-established educational publisher specialising in maths, English and science

Telling the time is a vital life skill. **Schofield & Sims Telling the Time** breaks this difficult topic down into a sequence of manageable ideas that young learners can approach at their own pace. Beginning with child-friendly explanations of times of day and units of time, the series moves on to introduce telling the time on an analogue clock, before progressing to cover a wide range of related concepts, including different ways of measuring and representing time, time expressions and everyday time problems.

Each activity book provides:

- large, clear clock faces for easy counting
- colour-coded hands to aid recognition of hours and minutes
- 'Learn' panels that explain time-telling in simple steps
- fun general-knowledge facts to enrich learning
- targeted practice, including counting activities, matching exercises, and drawing the hands on the clock
- answers to all the practice questions in the book.

Telling the Time 2 meets all the National Curriculum time requirements for Year 2. It covers counting in fives; telling the time to five minutes; units of time (including minutes, hours and days); ordering and comparing intervals of time; digital time; comparing analogue and digital clocks; and problem-solving using time.

Telling the Time 1   ISBN 978 07217 1418 9
Telling the Time 2   ISBN 978 07217 1419 6
Telling the Time 3   ISBN 978 07217 1420 2

Have you tried **Times Tables Practice** by Schofield & Sims?

This series of books gives children extensive practice in all the times tables relevant to their age group, providing enjoyable activities with attractive illustrations that will hold their attention throughout.

ISBN 978-07217-1419-6

MIX
Paper from
responsible sources
FSC® C023114

9 780721 714196 >

For further information and to place your order visit
www.schofieldandsims.co.uk or telephone 01484 607080

ISBN 978 07217 1419 6
Key Stage 1
Age range 6–7 years
£3.50 (Retail price)